Daily Humor in Russian Life
Ежедневный Юмор в Русской Жизни

Russian caricatures with English translations
Русские карикатуры с английским переводом

Volume 6 - Our Smaller Brothers
Том 6 - Братья Наши Меньшие

Author: Foxy Dime
Автор: Фокси Дайм

FOXIT

Volume 6 - Our Smaller Brothers
Том 6 - Братья Наши Меньшие

Author: Foxy Dime
Автор: Фокси Дайм

This book is dedicated to the bright memory of my father, who inspired me to reach higher and never stop learning.

Эта книга посвящена светлой памяти моего отца, который вдохновлял меня достигать большего в жизни и никогда не прекращать учиться.

INTRODUCTION

The illustrations in this book were created by my father, who passed away in 2016. I decided to publish this series anonymously, since everything shared in this book, I hold very dear to my heart.

When we think about Russian animals, the first thought is probably a bear in the Russian circus. Traditionally animals were not treated kindly in the Soviet Union. Of course, that does not apply to everyone. I am very happy to see that animal cruelty laws finally passed in Russia. To quote Russian newspapers, "Russian President Vladimir Putin is certain that the articles of responsible treatment of animals should be enshrined in the Russian constitution as a manifestation of civility."

Our family loves animals. We always have cats, dogs, fish … you name it. The caricatures in this book do not include cruel animal treatment humor. Instead, caricatures capture funny, kind humor in everyday Russian life that included animals. When the book refers to the animals, it includes not only actual animals, but also fictional animals and animals in Russian folk tales.

Just like the caricatures in this book, even with your own pets, when they cause mischief, strike a pose, or even chew your favorite shoes you cannot stay mad at them for too long; you start smiling and eventually start laughing.

So, hug your pet or think of an animal you love and start enjoying yet another volume of Russian caricatures.

ВСТУПЛЕНИЕ

Иллюстрации в этой книге нарисованы моим отцом, который скончался в 2016 году. Я решила опубликавать эту книгу анонимно, так как содержимое этой книги очень близко и дорого моему сердцу.

Когда мы думаем о русских животных, первое, что приходит в голову, это медведь в цирке. В советское время люди не относились к животным с добротой. Конечно, это относится не ко всем. Я очень рада, что наконец в России был принят закон о гуманном и ответственном обращении с животными. По цитате газеты "Закрепление в Конституции России нормы об ответственном отношении к животным в обществе востребовано обществом, считает президент России Владимир Путин."

Наша семья всегда любила животных. У нас всегда в доме водилась и водится всякая живность - кошки, собаки, рыбы и всякая другая живность. В карикатурах этой книги вы не найдёте юмора о жестоком отношении к животным. Вместо этого, вы найдёте смешной и добрый юмор, который вклычает животных в каждодневной жизни. Когда эта книга рассказывает о животных, это означает не только живых животных, но и вымышленных животных из русских сказок и фольклора.

Как и в карикатурах этой книги, наши питомцы иногда выкидывают всякие фокусы, принимают позу или разгрызают нашу любимую обувь. Мы не можем на них долго сердится, мы начинаем улыбаться и смеятся.

Ну давайте, обнимите вашего питомца или подумайте о нём или о ней, и начните наслаждаться этим томом карикатур.

CARICATURES

КАРИКАТУРЫ

-Here you go! Mowgli remembered that he is human!

-Papa, if a lion gets out of the cage and eats you, what bus should I take home?

-Come in, don't be afraid, the dog is neutered…
-That's why I think he will bite me!

-Grandma, the Australian grasshoppers are much bigger than ours, do you not agree?

-Can you please take black and white picture for us?

-Don't worry darling, we will make the cat walk back…
(In reference to a black cat crossing the road)

-Oh, what a beautiful dog! Does she bite?
-The dog doesn't bite, but master fights!

-Before you go hunting, kill the beast within you...!

-This's the time I shot the rabbit…

-Mam, where did I come from?
-The stork brought you to us… Just don't tell your papa…!

-If labor turns us into them, then I'm refusing to clean my cage…

In reference to the Russian fairytale: "The Golden Fish"

Stone writing: "If you ride to the left, you will lose your horse, if you ride to the right, you will lose your head". -Vanya, let's go home… We have beer, and neighbor Klava… Maybe there is something for me….

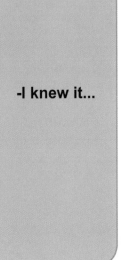

-I knew it...

-Mama, look
the angels
are flying...

-See my son,
these people
think we're
idiots...
Honest to
god, they
think like
little
children...

-Are you the wife of grandpa Mazay...? (In reference to "Grandfather Mazay and hares")

-How do you like this? I send him to get a newspaper, instead he goes to kitchen to cook dinner…!

-Are you sure my ancestors were sailors…?

-Do ostriches lose their feathers?
-They usually don't, but they could drop a few if they see 200 rubles…

-Malvina, did the stork bring me too…?
-No, a woodpecker brought you.

-Are you hot? Maybe you can use a quick swim?

-What happen with your camel?
-That's my wife learning to ride…

-Say "rabbit", otherwise you will get sucked in…

Sign: "Recycle collection unit"

-Where did the two females go? They were just here…

-How many times can I tell you: "Don't eat those nitrates! at least during pregnancy"

-Don't you recognize me? I'm from Tambov. (There is an idiom in Russia: «Тамбовский волк тебе товарищ» which can be understood as "Don't comrade me")

-Watson, Sir Baskerville paid us in full; it's time to find different owner for the dog (In reference to "Hound of the Baskervilles" by Arthur Conan Doyle)

-Papa, when will I become rich?
-When you will become a wallet, my baby…

-Listen, hen, there are Pokemons hatching from the eggs now...

-Old man, if you won't let me go, I will mess up your first three wishes. (In reference to Russian Fairytale: "The Golden Fish")

-If your wife is still alive, you can eat me... (In reference to Russian Fairytale: "The Golden Fish")

-Why are you peeing in aquarium?
-These are salt water fish; they will feel right at home.

-Go check and see what is that noise in the bushes...?
-Who knows, what if it jumps?

-Confess, what are you hiding in your humps?

-My son, here is mama bear, there is papa bear and the little son bear...
-Aha! Where is aunt Lyba?

-Adam, why is the snake suspiciously green and without an apple...?

-Dear God turn the lion into a Christian!
-Dear God, Bless this meal!

-Crocodile Gena, it looks like you're a chameleon; you turned all blue… (In reference to soviet cartoon series "Cheburashka and friends"

-Can you please tell me your name?
-No, stuff your face without it!

Writing on the trap: "Come, Jim, give me your paw for luck …" -Maybe I should? (In reference to poem by Russian poet Sergey Yesenin)

-What, there isn't enough space in your pouch? (In reference to Russian saying "not for your pocket" and play on the words "pocket" both for pants pocket and kangaroo pouch also refers as "pocket")

-Did you enjoy the movie?
-No, the book was better…

-Don't sell the skin till you have caught the bear, it's inhumane!

-Are you squeamish?

-If you want to have all your wishes come true, carry a gun! (In reference to Russian folk tale Emelya and the Pike)

-Aha!
-Am I going
die now?
(In reference
to a novel by
Eugene
Onegin)

-Grandma, did these monsters attacked you when you were a little girl?

-Red Riding Hood, aren't you afraid to walk in this dark forest?
-Why should I be afraid? I know the road and I love the sex!

-Just like in a restaurant, on the tray with the napkin!

-Wise Kaa, I came to ask your advice…
-Hey boy, don't bug the python. If you want, we can take your picture; if you don't have money then go away…!

-Old man, hurry, cast your net and get me out of here… (In reference to Russian Fairytale: "The Golden Fish")

-Don't crowd they are asking for me…

-Don't pull the cat's tail! -He is pulling it; I'm just holding his tail…

-I see how you water down the milk…

-What a cute bundle of fur; who do we have here? Cat or kitten?
-Rabbit…!

-I can't train the silly fish to take flakes from my hand…!

-The captain thinks he knows everything, but we know more…!

-I can't figure out what Pegasus is hinting at?

-Vanya, we're brothers now, we ate the rabbit and the duck and we will keep the needle in your egg. (In reference to Russian folk tale "Koschei the Deathless")

-I will wait until you turn into a girl before I marry you... I'm concerned with bad habits and attitudes...

-Who's knocking? You aren't letting me sleep. Tomorrow I have to work night shift.

-The Frenchmen invited me to the date in restaurant...!

-Mother locked us in and hung the key on the tree!

-I ate the tourist from Russia!
-You're lying! Quickly breath in here.

-Why knock if there is a door bell?!

-Grey wolf, why do you have such big...
-So, it will be better for you Red Riding Hood...

-Drink my brother, you will turn into a human... (In reference to "Sister Alyonushka and Brother Ivanushka" Russian folk tale)

-I won't sell the golden fish to an old craw. (In reference to Russian Fairytale: "The Golden Fish")

-To make me they scraped out the flour-box and swept out the bin, - dirt, dust, cigarette butts... Don't eat me!
(In reference to Russian folk tale "The little round bun (Kolobok)")

-Why are you standing there, serve the second course...

-Check it out, the hut laid an egg…!

-Son, who's the king of animals?
-The zoo owner!

-Vanka, bastard, you're going to kill me…

-Vasya, if they catch us, they will kick me out of my house…

-Vasya, did you spend your paycheck on alcohol again…
-Look, how shamelessly they thought the bird to curse…

-Take me to the rich house!

-Yesterday Mumu bought flippers and a breathing tube, today books, does she want to be Darwin? (In reference to "Mumu" a short story by Ivan Turgenev)

-Red Riding Hood, you can call me grandpa…

-Everyone travels like "rabbits", I'm not a red head either…
(In reference to passengers who travel without a ticket have the nickname "rabbits")

-Don't come out, the old woman is going crazy! (In reference to Russian Fairytale: "The Golden Fish")

-I'm sorry old man; I don't understand Chinese…
(In reference to Russian Fairytale: "The Golden Fish")

-First you need to feed pigs, then build a pig house, then you need to plant an oak…
(In reference to Muslim saying that man needs to have a son, build a house and raise a tree)

-Don't be stupid, storks don't bring tadpoles.

-If you want to boss me around, then become a Sheppard…

-Just you look at what is going on… I don't have a fur coat, but he is petting the dog….

CONCLUSION

Our passion is to spread the knowledge of the mysterious Russian language. We created educational and entertaining materials for learning Russian. You can find our educational materials in both printed and digital format on our website, on Amazon, Amazon Kindle, Apple Books, Barnes and Nobles, and Google play books. Be sure to visit our website for more information!

Our Website	https://foxitdimensions.com/
FoxIT Russian Alphabet Cards	https://foxitdimensions.com/russian-alphabet-cards.html
FoxIT Russian Alphabet Poster	https://foxitdimensions.com/russian-alphabet-poster.html
FoxIT Russian Alphabet Book	https://foxitdimensions.com/russian-alphabet-book.html

Daily Humor in Russian Life Series	https://foxitdimensions.com/russian-humor-books.html
Volume 1 - Mix	https://foxitdimensions.com/daily-humor-in-russian-life-volume-1.html
Volume 2 - Mix	https://foxitdimensions.com/daily-humor-in-russian-life-volume-2.html
Volume 3 - Alcohol Edition	https://foxitdimensions.com/daily-humor-in-russian-life-volume-3.html
Volume 4 - Rated "R" edition	https://foxitdimensions.com/daily-humor-in-russian-life-volume-4.html
Volume 5 - Beware of doctors	https://foxitdimensions.com/daily-humor-in-russian-life-volume-5.html
Volume 6 - Our Smaller Brothers	https://foxitdimensions.com/daily-humor-in-russian-life-volume-6.html
Volume 7 - Watch Out Children	https://foxitdimensions.com/daily-humor-in-russian-life-volume-7.html
Volume 8 - Love and Marriage	https://foxitdimensions.com/daily-humor-in-russian-life-volume-8.html
Volume 9 - Woman's Touch	https://foxitdimensions.com/daily-humor-in-russian-life-volume-9.html
Volume 10 - Man's Power	https://foxitdimensions.com/daily-humor-in-russian-life-volume-10.html
Volume 11 - Eat and Drink	https://foxitdimensions.com/daily-humor-in-russian-life-volume-11.html
Volume 12 - Man vs Woman	https://foxitdimensions.com/daily-humor-in-russian-life-volume-12.html
Volume 13 - Mix	https://foxitdimensions.com/daily-humor-in-russian-life-volume-13.html
Volume 14 - Mix	https://foxitdimensions.com/daily-humor-in-russian-life-volume-14.html

ЗАКЛЮЧЕНИЕ

Наша миссия - это распространять знание таинственного русского языка. Мы создали учебные и занимательные материалы для изучения русского языка. Вы можете приобрести их в книжном или электронном формате на нашем сайте, на Амазоне, на сайте книжного магазина Barnes and Noble, в книжных магазинах Google (EBooks) и Apple (IBooks). Читайте подробности на нашем сайте.

Наш сайт	https://foxitdimensions.com/
Русские Алфавитные Карточки	https://foxitdimensions.com/russian-alphabet-cards.html
Постер с Русским Алфавитом	https://foxitdimensions.com/russian-alphabet-poster.html
Книга Русский Алфавит	https://foxitdimensions.com/russian-alphabet-book.html

Ежедневный Юмор в Русской Жизни	https://foxitdimensions.com/russian-humor-books.html
Том 1 - Ассорти	https://foxitdimensions.com/daily-humor-in-russian-life-volume-1.html
Том 2 - Ассорти	https://foxitdimensions.com/daily-humor-in-russian-life-volume-2.html
Том 3 - Алкогольное Издание	https://foxitdimensions.com/daily-humor-in-russian-life-volume-3.html
Том 4 - Издание с рейтингом «16+»	https://foxitdimensions.com/daily-humor-in-russian-life-volume-4.html
Том 5 - Берегитесь врачей	https://foxitdimensions.com/daily-humor-in-russian-life-volume-5.html
Том 6 - Братья Наши Меньшие	https://foxitdimensions.com/daily-humor-in-russian-life-volume-6.html
Том 7 - Осторожно Дети	https://foxitdimensions.com/daily-humor-in-russian-life-volume-7.html
Том 8 - Любовь и Женитьба	https://foxitdimensions.com/daily-humor-in-russian-life-volume-8.html
Том 9 - Прикосновение Женщины	https://foxitdimensions.com/daily-humor-in-russian-life-volume-9.html
Том 10 - Мужская Сила	https://foxitdimensions.com/daily-humor-in-russian-life-volume-10.html
Том 11 - Ешь и Закусывай	https://foxitdimensions.com/daily-humor-in-russian-life-volume-11.html
Том 12 - Мужчина против женщины	https://foxitdimensions.com/daily-humor-in-russian-life-volume-12.html
Том 13 - Ассорти	https://foxitdimensions.com/daily-humor-in-russian-life-volume-13.html
Том 14 - Ассорти	https://foxitdimensions.com/daily-humor-in-russian-life-volume-14.html

Printed in Great Britain
by Amazon